COLOR YOUR WAY TO BETTER FOCUS

# ART FOR MINDFULNESS
# OWLS AND OTHER BIRDS

PATTERNS BY CHRIS TOMLIN

HarperCollins*Publishers*
1 London Bridge Street
London SE1 9GF
www.harpercollins.co.uk

First published by HarperCollins*Publishers* in 2016
1 3 5 7 9 10 8 6 4 2

Patterns by Chris Tomlin
Introduction text by Imi Lo

Library of Congress Cataloging-in-Publication Data available upon request.

ISBN 978-0-00-795195-6

Printed and bound in China

# Introduction

**M**indfulness has become extremely popular in recent years, as scientists discover more about the wide array of benefits it has to offer—reducing stress, increasing joy, enhancing emotional intelligence, and undoing bad habits. Although it can be defined in various ways, mindfulness is most simply described as approaching the present moment non-judgmentally, and with curiosity. It offers a break from our incessant, autopilot mind and provides the opportunity to live a fuller life.

Despite urban myth, mindfulness practice is not simply about sitting uncomfortably or chanting "Omm." *Art for Mindfulness* lies in the intersection of mindfulness and therapeutic art, offering a doorway into mindfulness that is accessible, relatable, and fun. Feeling burdened by the chaos of modern life, many adults have found that coloring helps them reconnect with a simpler, more spontaneous way of being.

In order to reap the most benefits from this book, I would invite you to approach it with a playful and curious attitude. A few partially colored-in patterns follow for use as inspiration before you embark on your own work. However, despite what your art teacher may have told you in school, there is absolutely no right or wrong way of coloring. You may be pleasantly surprised by the outcome when you trust your instinct and allow color and strokes to naturally unfold; you may discover a deep sense of calm when you begin to pay the activity your full attention. You may also find this to be a great way to develop more soulful connections with those around you. I hope that you not only enjoy this book, but also discover a deeper layer of spiritual practice through immersing in the art of mindful coloring.

Imi Lo (UKCP, HCPC, MMH), Art Psychotherapist and Mindfulness Teacher

**"The owl is the wisest of all birds because the more it sees, the less it talks."**

African proverb

**"The true miracle lies in our eagerness to allow, appreciate, and honor the uniqueness and freedom of each sentient being to sing the song of their heart."**

Amit Ray

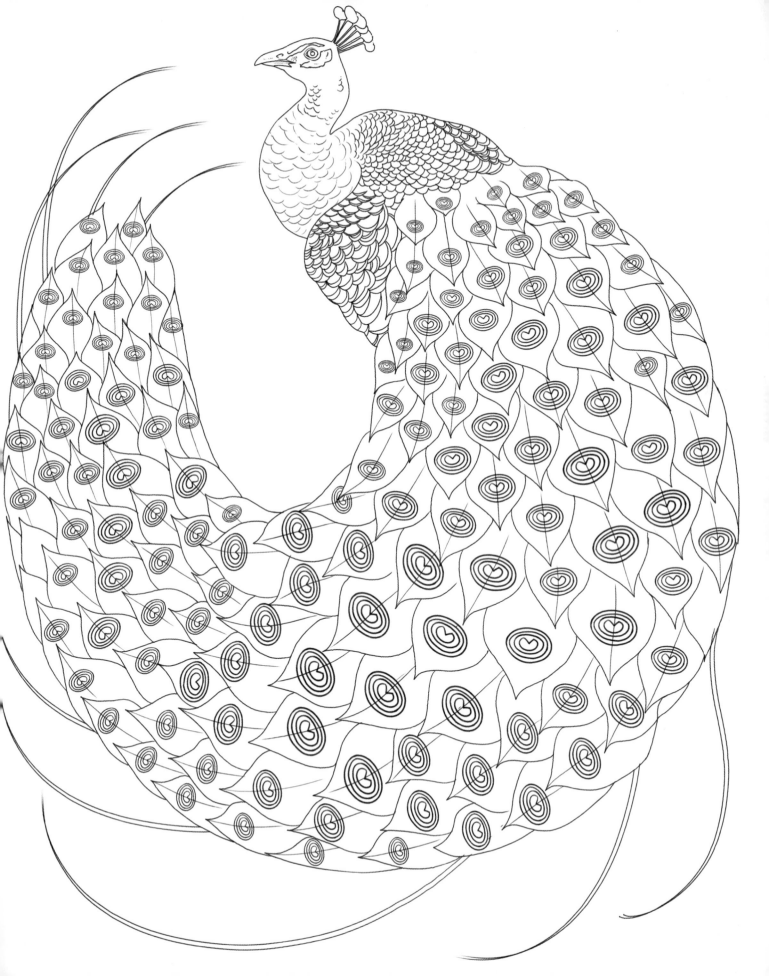

# "Wisdom begins in wonder."

Socrates

**"I want to sing like the birds sing, not worrying about who hears or what they think."**

Rumi

# "Adopt the pace of nature: her secret is patience."

Ralph Waldo Emerson

# "Change your thoughts and you change the world."

Norman Vincent Peale

**"The two most powerful warriors are patience and time."**

Leo Tolstoy

# "A bird does not sing because it has an answer. It sings because it has a song."

Chinese proverb

# "What you are is what you have been. What you'll be is what you do now."

Buddha

**"Don't believe what your eyes are telling you. All they show is limitation. Look with your understanding, find out what you already know, and you'll see the way to fly."**

Richard Bach

**"The clearest way into the universe is through a forest wilderness."**

John Muir

# "The higher we soar, the smaller we appear to those who cannot fly."

Friedrich Nietzsche

"A wise old owl sat on an oak.
The more he saw, the less he spoke.
The less he spoke, the more he heard.
Why can't we be like that wise old bird?"

Charles M. Schulz

# "Quiet the mind, and the soul will speak."

Ma Jaya Sati Bhagavati

# "The amount of happiness you have depends on the amount of freedom you have in your heart."

Thích Nhất Hạnh

# "Flying is learning how to throw yourself at the ground and miss."

Douglas Adams

# "Patience is the companion of wisdom."

Saint Augustine

# "Eternity is not future or past. Eternity is a dimension of now."

Joseph Campbell

# "Knowledge speaks, but wisdom listens."

Jimi Hendrix

"An awake heart is like a sky that pours light."

Hāfez

**"Meditation is the dissolution of thoughts in Eternal awareness or Pure consciousness without objectification, knowing without thinking, merging finitude in infinity."**

Voltaire

"If we sit with an increasing stillness of the body, and attune our mind to the sky or to the ocean or to the myriad stars at night, or any other indicators of vastness, the mind gradually stills and the heart is filled with quiet joy."

Ravi Ravindra

# "Self-observation is the first step of inner unfolding."

Amit Ray

## "Meditation is nothing but taking a mental shower."

Yogi Bhajan

"If you are silent through meditation, utterly silent, suddenly you feel a tremendous urge to create something."

Osho

# "When we meditate, we expand, spreading our wings like a bird."

Sri Chinmoy

**"Keep your heart clear and transparent, and you will never be bound. A single disturbed thought creates ten thousand distractions."**

Ryōkan

# "Be creative.
# Men only learnt how to fly when they stopped imitating birds."

Paulo Coelho

# "The act of meditation is being spacious."

Sogyal Rinpoche

**"Wisdom is not a product of schooling, but of the lifelong attempt to acquire it."**

Albert Einstein

# "Experience is not what happens to you; it's what you do with what happens to you."

Aldous Huxley

# "Meditation is the soul's perspective glass."

Owen Feltham

# "The future is always beginning now."

Mark Strand

"Be as a bird perched on a frail branch that she feels bending beneath her, still she sings away all the same, knowing she has wings."

Victor Hugo

# "Meditation is the tongue of the soul and the language of our spirit."

Jeremy Taylor

# "The only true wisdom is in knowing you know nothing."

Socrates

# "Feelings are just visitors, let them come and go."

Mooji

# "The doorstep to the temple of wisdom is knowledge of our own ignorance."

Benjamin Franklin

**"Faith is the bird that feels the light when the dawn is still dark."**

Rabindranath Tagore

# "Happiness, not in another place, but this place . . . not for another hour, but this hour."

Walt Whitman

"Empty your mind, be formless, shapeless—like water. Now you put water into a cup, it becomes the cup, you put water into a bottle, it becomes the bottle, you put it in a teapot, it becomes the teapot. Now water can flow or it can crash. Be water, my friend."

Bruce Lee

"You've got to think about big things while you're doing small things, so that all the small things go in the right direction."

Alvin Toffler

**"When meditation is mastered, the mind is unwavering like the flame of a candle in a windless place."**

*The Bhagavad Gita*

# "No bird soars too high if he soars with his own wings."

William Blake

# "The bird who dares to fall is the bird who learns to fly."

Unknown

**"There is a wisdom of the head and a wisdom of the heart."**

Charles Dickens

"If the mind falls asleep, awaken it. Then if it starts wandering, make it quiet. If you reach the state where there is neither sleep nor movement of mind, stay still in that, the natural (real) state."

Ramana Maharshi

**"The art of being wise is the art of knowing what to overlook."**

William James

"She went out on a limb,
had it break off behind her,
and realized she could fly."

Kobi Yamada

# "Don't refuse to go on an occasional wild goose chase—that's what wild geese are for."

Unknown

# "There are three values: feel good, be good, and do good."

Yogi Bhajan

**"Calm the winds of your thoughts, and there will be no waves on the ocean of your mind."**

Remez Sasson

# "If I keep a green bough in my heart, a singing bird will come."

Chinese proverb

**"When you realize how perfect everything is, you will tilt your head back and laugh at the sky."**

Buddha

"No bird can fly without opening its wings, and no one can love without exposing their hearts."

Mark Nepo

**"Give the ones you love wings to fly, roots to come back, and reasons to stay."**

Dalai Lama

# "Honesty is the first chapter in the book of wisdom."

Thomas Jefferson

"Stop the words now.
Open the window in the
center of your chest and let
the spirits fly in and out."

Rumi

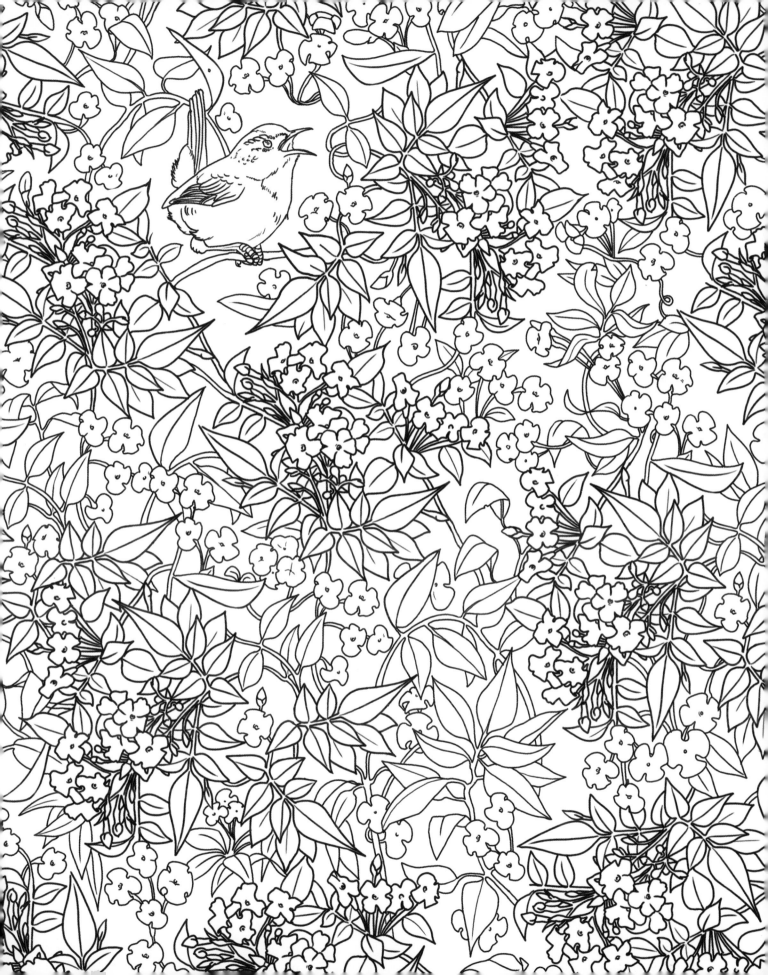

# "Don't you know yet? It is your light that lights the worlds."

Rumi

**"Your vision will become clear only when you can look into your own heart."**

Carl Jung